Raintree is an imprint of Capstone Global Library Limited, a company incorporated in England and Wales having its registered office at 264 Banbury Road, Oxford, OX2 7DY – Registered company number: 6695582
www.raintree.co.uk
myorders@raintree.co.uk

Edited by Heidi Hogg
Design and production by Nikki Farinella
Original illustrations © Capstone Global Library Limited 2016
Originated by Capstone Global Library Limited
Printed and bound in China

ISBN 978 1 4747 3679 4
20 19 18 17 16
10 9 8 7 6 5 4 3 2 1

British Library Cataloguing in Publication Data
A full catalogue record for this book is available from the British Library.

Acknowledgements
We would like to thank the following for permission to reproduce photographs: Alamy: Pictorial Press Ltd., 19; AP Images: STR, 32, *The Columbus Dispatch*/Lon Horwedel, 35; Getty Images: Bettmann, 28-29 (bottom), 34, Corbis/George Rinhart, 31, Popperfoto/Rolls Press, 38, University of Cambridge/Scott Polar Research Institute/Herbert Ponting, 30; iStockphoto: Bombaert, 16, Sami Suni, 13, szymanskim, 8; NASA, 39, 40, 41; Newscom: Ambient Images/Philip Scalia, 22, Glasshouse Images, 36, picture-alliance, 25, Stapleton Historical Collection Heritage Images, 26-27, World History Archive, 7, 14; North Wind Picture Archives, 10, 20; Rare Books and Special Collections (RBSC)/University of British Columbia Library, 5; Red Line Editorial, 9, 21, 37; Shutterstock: BestGreenScreen, 33, edella, 24, gowri varanashi, 18, Kamil Martinovsky, 23, Kotomiti Okuma, 27 (right); SuperStock: Everett Collection, 6, Pantheon, 11, 12, Pantheon/Mar/Illustrated London News Ltd, 28 (top), Science and Society, 17, The Art Archive, 15, World History Archive, 4; U.S. Coast Guard photo by Mike Brodey, cover

Design Element: Shutterstock Images: Designer things (bursts, dots, and bubble cloud)

CONTENTS

MISTAKEN MAPS

EXPLORATION ERRORS!

People mess things up all the time. Small slip-ups, such as getting a little lost or sneezing really loudly, might go unnoticed if you're near home. But what if you're an explorer lost on the open seas or a climber in an avalanche zone? Then you might be in trouble! Since ancient times, brave travellers have left their homes and set out to explore the unknown. History books are full of stories of successful accomplishments. But what about the failures, disasters and plain old stupid mistakes? Get ready for the blooper reel of world exploration.

FLAT OR ROUND?

Thousands of years ago, most people believed that the world was flat. In fact, ancient civilizations believed if you travelled far enough, you might fall right off the edge! Greek scholars had worked out the truth by 500 BC. But even today, some people refuse to believe it. Their theory is that Earth is flat, and we're all trapped under a giant glass dome.

Created in the 900s, this Anglo-Saxon map shows the ocean surrounding Earth.

DRAGON

This Japanese map, called *Jishin no ben*, shows the areas devastated by an earthquake in red.

FAST FACT

Some old maps contained sketches of dragons and other fantastic creatures. An 1855 map of Japan has a picture of a dragon as a way to explain an earthquake.

IT'S A SMALL WORLD

Eratosthenes was a Greek scholar who lived during the 200s and 100s BC. He thought the world just got colder and colder to the north and hotter and hotter to the south. About 350 years later, the astronomer and cartographer Ptolemy expanded and improved the world map. But since he lived in Egypt, he didn't know about North America or South America. He just filled in the unknown regions with doodles of land. He also got the size of the planet wrong – his Earth was far too small.

Even today you can discover something that's not on a map yet. Heavy rains created a new sandbar by the Channel Islands of California, USA, in 2005. A ship called the *Irving Johnson* found it – and the discovery caused more than £1.5 million in damages to the vessel.

OOPS!

IMAGINARY ISLANDS

Have you ever made something up to impress somebody? Well, Benjamin Morrell (1795–1839) invented islands – more than 100 of them! This American explorer of the 1800s was in serious debt after four voyages. Hoping to cash in on the public's fascination with faraway places, Morrell wrote about his travels. He recorded finding numerous new islands, including New South Greenland. His discoveries ended up on naval charts and atlases. Decades later people started to realize that these places didn't actually exist!

Spanish priest Antonio de la Ascensión went on a voyage from Mexico to explore the coast of California in 1602. For some reason he noted that the Mediterranean Sea of California separated the area from the mainland. For more than 100 years, mapmakers drew California as an island!

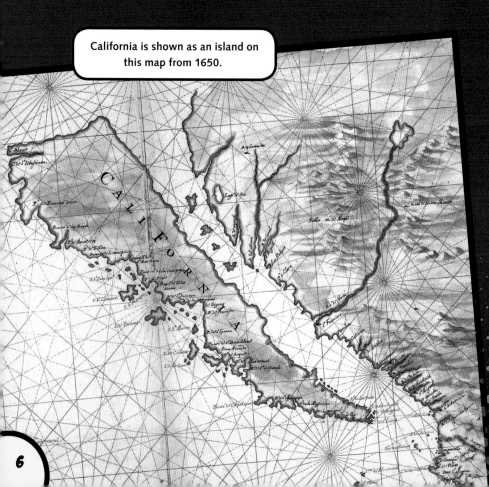

California is shown as an island on this map from 1650.

6

Not long before supposedly discovering New South Greenland, Morrell spent 16 days searching in vain for the Aurora Islands. A shame Morrell didn't know beforehand that the Aurora Islands were also imaginary!

MAKING MOUNTAINS OUT OF MOLEHILLS

On most maps of Africa made in the 1800s, the Mountains of Kong stretched across the Sahara desert. But the area is all desert, with no mountains at all. It turns out this was probably just idle gossip that got out of control. Most likely, local people told Scottish explorer Mungo Park (1771–1806) about a group of hills, and these hills grew into mountains as the information passed from person to person.

Mungo Park's misinformation showed up on maps for nearly 100 years.

During the summer of 2010, people trying to get to the city of Sunrise, Florida, USA, ran into trouble. For a whole month, this city of more than 90,000 people was missing from Google Maps.

OOPS!

ANCIENT EXPLORERS

MYSTERY MOUNTAIN

In the 400s BC, two explorers – Himilco and Hanno – left the city of Carthage in northern Africa. Himilco explored the coast of Europe. On his way home, the wind died, and his ship got stuck in a sea of weeds. Some say he blamed the delay on sea monsters too.

Hanno sailed south along the coast of Africa. He wrote that he passed a mountain full of fire with flames pouring into the sea. Experts today bicker like schoolchildren about this. The giant volcano Mount Cameroon lies along the coast of Africa, but many historians say he never could have made it that far. They say Hanno must have seen Mount Kakulima in Guinea instead. So exactly where was this mountain of fire that Hanno described as so high it touched the stars? No one knows for sure.

Hanno probably never saw an eruption of Mount Cameroon (below).

Note to self: when travelling to Russia, don't take camels! In the AD 900s, Ahmad ibn Fadlan travelled from the Middle East into what is now Russia. At one point, ibn Fadlan's camels had to trudge through snow that came up to their knees!

OOPS!

MISSION ALMOST IMPOSSIBLE

Many early explorers travelled the Silk Road, a trade route that connected Asia, northern Africa, the Middle East and Europe. Zhang Qian, a Chinese diplomat in the 100s BC, was one of the trailblazers of the Silk Road. But he almost didn't make it. He was captured on his very first adventure and held prisoner for 10 years. Talk about a long visit! When he finally escaped, he went straight back to his mission.

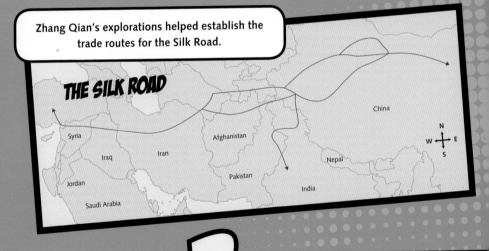

Zhang Qian's explorations helped establish the trade routes for the Silk Road.

THE SILK ROAD

Syria
Iraq
Jordan
Saudi Arabia
Iran
Afghanistan
Pakistan
India
Nepal
China

N
W E
S

DID YOU KNOW?

Marco Polo is famous for leaving his home in Venice, Italy, to travel to Asia in 1271. He thought he had discovered unicorns and man-eating serpents there. But really the animals were just rhinoceroses and crocodiles.

PERIL ON THE HIGH SEAS

USELESS MAP

In 1492 Columbus sailed the ocean blue. Christopher Columbus was one of many European explorers in the 1400s and 1500s. These people set sail seeking new trade routes or new lands to claim for kings and queens back home in Europe. Problems plagued these voyages. Navigation mistakes sent explorers far off their marks. Storms at sea wrecked ships or blew them off course. On long trips across the sea, crews often ran short of food and water. When Christopher Columbus arrived in the Bahamas, he thought he was in Asia, thanks to Ptolemy's mistaken map. He even called the people he met "Indians", after the East Indies.

On his voyage, Christopher Columbus stood onboard the *Santa Maria*, awaiting sight of the New World.

Some say Leif Eriksson's brother Thorvald was killed by American Indians when he tried to settle there.

DID YOU KNOW?

The Vikings reached North America nearly 500 years before Columbus. Leif Eriksson started a settlement on the coast of what is now Canada. But the Vikings weren't very good at making friends with the native people who already lived there. The settlement was soon abandoned.

A THREE-MONTH TOUR

Ferdinand Magellan departed from Spain in 1519 on the first voyage to sail around the globe. It was Magellan who gave the Pacific Ocean its name because he thought it appeared so calm and pleasant. So everything was smooth sailing? Hardly.

Magellan was wrong about how long it would take to cross the Pacific Ocean. He had estimated three days. Instead, it took more than three months! Many sailors starved. The crew made several attempts to take leadership away from the captain. Magellan left two of these mutineers behind on an island. But then he met his death when a native shot him with a poison arrow in the Philippines. Just one ship out of five and 18 of the original 237 sailors returned to Spain in 1522.

UNDERCOVER PIRATES!

Pirates were a real threat to many sea voyages. They usually didn't bury their treasure or make people walk the plank. But some did wear earrings because they thought it would prevent seasickness. And if someone crossed them? Lucky victims were marooned on a small island. Unlucky types got tied to the boat, thrown overboard and dragged under the ship.

Some pirates were also explorers. Sir Francis Drake was the first English captain to make it all the way around the globe. He was also the first Englishman to land in what is now California, USA. On the side, he attacked Spanish ships. These ships often carried gold or other valuables from the New World. But Drake wasn't in it for the treasure – at least, not for himself. Secretly, he was working for Queen Elizabeth I. She even made him a knight for his efforts, which royally annoyed the king of Spain.

Not every English pirate was knighted. In fact, some were beheaded instead.

Everyone knows that a skull and crossbones on a black flag means pirates. This flag is called the Jolly Roger. Not very jolly, though, is it?

Legend has it that if the pirates' flag was red instead of black, it meant the ship would take no prisoners alive!

FINDERS KEEPERS?

One of those gold-laden Spanish ships, the *San Jose*, sank off the coast of Colombia in 1708. Experts today estimate that its cargo of gold and emeralds is worth as much as £13 billion! Treasure hunters have finally found the ship, but they're fighting over who gets the treasure.

DID YOU KNOW?

Packing for a sea voyage? Don't forget the limes! Many early explorers perished from a disease called scurvy. Doctors eventually realized that a lack of vitamin C causes the disease. Seafarers simply had to drink lime juice to get enough of the vitamin. People started calling sailors "limeys".

FAST FACT

Abel Tasman of the Netherlands explored the South Pacific in the 1640s. On his first voyage, he discovered Tasmania, New Zealand and the Fiji Islands. But he somehow missed Australia! He spotted the giant continent on the next trip.

UNWELCOME GUESTS

Explorers didn't typically "discover" a new country or island. When a ship arrived at a destination, the travellers usually found people already living there. Sometimes the native people invited the explorers to dinner. At other times, the explorers became the dinner.

Explorers also set out from many parts of the world – not just Europe. Almost 100 years before Columbus set sail, a Chinese explorer named Zheng He journeyed to Southeast Asia, the Middle East and Africa. Among other valuable trade goods, the missions brought giraffes, zebras, oryxes (antelopes) and other animals back to China. But when the emperor of China died, his successor did not value exploration. The Chinese government made a drastic move in 1525. It proclaimed that all seafaring ships must be destroyed. That was a bad day for exploration and discovery!

Zheng He's sailing charts were finally published in 1628.

If bad weather hadn't forced him to turn around, Cook might not have perished in Hawaii.

TROUBLE IN PARADISE

English explorer James Cook may have been the first European to visit the islands of Hawaii. During his second visit, he happened to show up during a festival celebrating Lono, a local god. So the natives welcomed him and his men as gods. Cook didn't bother to correct their mistake. The Europeans spent a month living it up in paradise. But when one of Cook's men died, the natives got suspicious. Cook tried to leave but was forced to return after a storm damaged his ships. A pity there wasn't another god he could pretend to be. The natives attacked and killed him.

In 1961 American Michael Rockefeller was exploring New Guinea in search of native art when his boat flipped over. He swam for shore, and no one heard from him again. The leading theory is that cannibals killed and ate him.

OOPS!

JUNGLE EXPEDITIONS

Canoes are still used today on the River Niger in Mali.

CANOE PIRATES

In Africa and South America, explorers ventured into dense jungles and rainforests. Hacking a path through thick vegetation wasn't easy. Plus poisonous snakes, hungry beasts and deadly parasites lurked around every bend. So travelling on boats down rivers seemed like a good idea. Except rivers weren't exactly safe, either. Some pirates travelled by canoe. British brothers Richard and John Lander were mapping the River Niger in Africa in 1830 when river pirates took them prisoner. No Europeans were around to pay a ransom. So the pirates sold them to a local trader. The brothers eventually escaped.

Englishwoman Mary Henrietta Kingsley may have been the only person to explore the African jungle wearing a dress and petticoats. Once she accidentally fell into a pit meant for catching game. It was lined with spikes. She wrote in 1897 that her thick skirt saved her!

OOPS!

DID YOU KNOW?

The wife of famous explorer David Livingstone was killed by a lowly insect in 1862. A mosquito bite gave her malaria, a deadly disease. The mosquito actually causes more human deaths per year than any other animal.

David Livingstone (below) refused to return to England with Henry Morton Stanley and instead died in Africa less than two years later.

DINNER AND A SHOW

Scottish explorer David Livingstone (1813–1873) set out to find the beginning of the River Nile in Africa in 1865. But many of his crew were not up for the task. They abandoned Livingstone and spread a rumour that he'd been murdered. Six years later newspaper reporter Henry Morton Stanley searched for him. He finally found him penniless in an African village. The local people found Livingstone's use of a fork and knife intriguing. They forced him to eat his meals in public so they could watch him. But Stanley's greeting became famous: "Dr. Livingstone, I presume?" Who else could it be?

GOLD FEVER

Piranhas, giant snakes and poison dart frogs – eek! The Amazon rainforest is a dangerous place. But rumours of a lost city of gold, called El Dorado, lured many explorers into the jungle.

One of the first to fail was Gonzalo Pizarro of Spain. He set out in 1541 with 200 soldiers in full armour on horseback, 4,000 slaves, and thousands of llamas, pigs and hunting dogs. A year later just 80 men returned – almost completely naked! Their clothing had rotted in the wet, hot rainforest.

Early Amazon explorers should have been less concerned about snakes and more worried about getting lost.

WELCOME HOME?

Fifty years later the English adventurer Sir Walter Raleigh led two expeditions to search for El Dorado. He survived the jungle but didn't get a very nice welcome-home present. King James I didn't like the fact that Sir Walter's crew had attacked a Spanish outpost. So the king had Raleigh beheaded!

LOST IN THE JUNGLE

By the 1900s some still believed in a lost city. Englishman Percy Fawcett vanished while searching for it in 1925. He got lost looking for a lost city!

In the decades since, more than 13 expeditions have failed to find out what happened to Fawcett. Brazilian businessman James Lynch tried to solve the mystery in 1996. His team took modern equipment, including GPS systems and walkie-talkies. But these tools didn't stop a native tribe from holding them all hostage until they handed over their expensive equipment.

This is the last known photo of Percy Fawcett before he disappeared into the Amazon.

FAST FACT

Many believe that El Dorado was just a legend. But Fawcett may have been on to something after all. New evidence shows that a lost city actually did exist in the Amazon. Satellites and aeroplanes have photographed the remains of roads and buildings. Was the city full of gold? No one yet knows.

RIVER VOYAGES

MAGIC FOUNTAINS

Ponce de León's second trip to Florida proved to be fatal.

Rivers helped explorers get from place to place in North America. However, encounters with wildlife, rapids and American Indians didn't always go as planned. Yet Europeans kept going to the New World. Many people wrongly think Juan Ponce de León of Spain was searching for the Fountain of Youth when he came to what is now the United States. The water of this mythical fountain supposedly made a person young again. Though he may have heard rumours of such a fountain, Ponce de León actually sought gold. He found some in the rivers of Puerto Rico. He should have stayed put. He went on to discover the US state of Florida in 1513, but later the native people killed him with a poison arrow.

Frenchman Louis Jolliet lost all of his notes and maps in 1674 after his canoe flipped over in rapids. He'd left a duplicate set in the town near Sainte-Marie Falls, so no worries, right? Wrong! The duplicates were burned in a fire. Talk about bad luck!

OOPS!

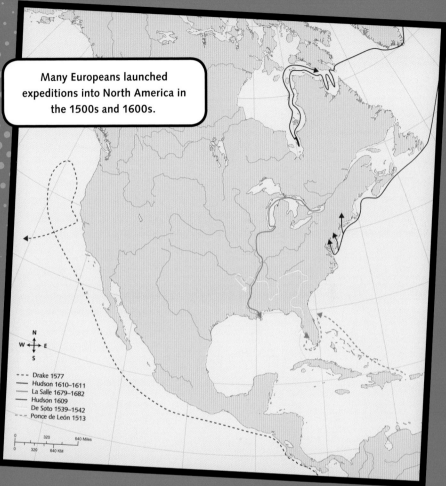

Many Europeans launched expeditions into North America in the 1500s and 1600s.

N
W E
S

- - - Drake 1577
—— Hudson 1610–1611
—— La Salle 1679–1682
—— Hudson 1609
—— De Soto 1539–1542
- - - Ponce de León 1513

0   320   640 Miles
0   320   640 KM

SHINY GOLD

Another Spanish explorer, Hernando de Soto amassed a treasure of gold, silver and gemstones in South America. But greed got the better of him. He took an army to North America in search of even more wealth. By 1541 he'd lost more than 200 men and more than 100 horses. Then de Soto got ill and died. His consolation prize? De Soto was the first European to discover the Mississippi River.

No gold? No problem – just make some up! French explorer Mathieu Sagean reported discovering the kingdom of Acaaniba in 1700 in what is now the southwestern United States. The people there made almost everything out of gold – from forks and spoons to entire palaces. But Acaaniba was just a fanciful story.

GO WITH THE ICE FLOE

Treasure wasn't for everybody. Some explorers had more practical goals. Many hoped that rivers or seas would provide a route across the North American continent. Then traders would be able to sail west from Europe all the way to Asia. Englishman Henry Hudson led many expeditions in the hope of finding such a route. But the third time wasn't lucky for this explorer. In 1609 he sailed up what became known as the Hudson River. Of course the river flows only the length of what is now New York State. On his fourth and last attempt in 1610, Hudson thought he'd finally made it to the Pacific when the coastline opened up. But it was just a gigantic bay. To make matters worse, on the way home from the failed voyage, Hudson's ship got stuck in ice. In the spring his angry crew set him adrift. He was never heard of again. But at least Hudson had a bay and a river named after him.

A replica of Hudson's ship the *Half Moon* sailed into the Hudson River in 2009.

r beavers! Americans Meriwether Lewis and
k caught lots of these furry beasts on their journey
n America in the early 1800s. One beaver decided
k. It bit their dog, Seaman. They worried the dog
survive. But Seaman pulled through. Tough dog!

look
y, but
heir
can

XT TIME, STOP FOR DIRECTIONS!

Frenchman René-Robert de la Salle explored the Mississippi River
orth America in the late 1600s. But he really could have done
n Google Maps. He led a group of settlers bound for Louisiana,
the group accidentally landed in Texas. There, an underwater reef
Spanish pirates sank two ships. They were stuck! The angry crew
tinied and shot de la Salle.

LOST IN THE DESERT

A BOAT IN THE DESERT

Deserts test travellers with sandstorms, scorching heat and a lack of food and water. Before trucks made desert crossings easier, explorers rode camels. But what did Heinrich Barth of Germany take on an 1850 expedition? A boat! His group brought the boat to explore Lake Chad in Africa.

BAD TIMING

Robert O'Hara Burke from Ireland took camels to an Australian desert in 1860. But the camels had more exploration experience than he did. At one point Burke got tired of waiting for supplies. He set out with a small group. The men left behind waited for four months and then abandoned base camp, taking the remaining food and water with them. Just eight hours later, Burke returned. Talk about bad timing.

Camels are not native to Australia and since being imported in the 1800s have become pests. The camels drink so much water that waterholes used by native people are drying up.

Sven Hedin probably should have spent more time planning his trip into the desert.

A SIP OF CAMEL PEE

Sven Hedin from Sweden led an expedition into the Taklimakan Desert in western China in 1895. At one point, the group thought they had enough water for 10 days. But someone got it wrong – they only had two days' worth. Instead of turning back, they pressed on. Desperate for water, the men drank camel pee!

DID YOU KNOW?

Camels can go without water for up to 160 kilometres (100 miles). But watch out – they spit! The stuff a camel spews out when upset actually contains vomit.

ICY MISHAPS

WHAT'S IN A NAME?

The North Pole and South Pole were two of the last places on Earth that explorers reached. For several centuries many voyages set out looking for a way to sail around the top of North America to get to Asia. But only a few ships ever completed the treacherous journey. Naming a ship the *Terror* doesn't bode well! Sir John Franklin led this ship and one other on a search for a Northwest Passage. The expedition set out from Britain in 1845 and was never heard from again. Numerous search parties tried to find them. One group even released Arctic foxes wearing collars bearing the location of a rescue ship. More than 150 years later, searchers finally found one of Franklin's ships. The *Terror* was found nearby in 2016.

Sir Francis McClintock spent most of his time from 1857 to 1859 searching the Arctic for John Franklin's lost expedition.

Early in his career, Sir John Franklin was on an expedition that ran out of food while exploring the Arctic. The British Navy officer ate lichen and leather from his own shoes!

TASTES LIKE CHICKEN

Food was scarce on these polar journeys. Vitus Bering from Denmark failed to find a Northwest Passage, but he found a large sea cow in the 1740s. Later expeditions hunted the delicious, easy-to-catch animal to extinction. Adrien de Gerlache from Belgium led an expedition to the Antarctic Circle in 1898 that ended up frozen in the ice. They survived by eating penguins!

Adrien de Gerlache thought penguins tasted terrible and initially declared them inedible.

While searching for the Northwest Passage in 1576, British explorer Martin Frobisher found a pile of black rocks on Baffin Island in Canada. Convinced that they contained gold, he took tonnes of the stuff back to England. But the rocks were worthless.

OOPS!

LIAR, LIAR

US Explorer Robert E. Peary reached the North Pole in 1909. Or did he? Scholars now believe he missed the mark by at least 50 kilometres (30 miles). But at least he wasn't actively trying to fool anyone.

Fellow American Frederick Cook seems to have set out to trick the world. First he faked climbing Mount McKinley in 1906. He even took photographs of the "summit". But a few years later, explorers found the exact same rocks depicted in the photo. Cook was 30 kilometres (20 miles) from the top. So it's no surprise that people were suspicious when he claimed to have reached the North Pole during a 1909 expedition!

Frederick Cook took this photo during his North Pole expedition, showing the igloo he stayed in.

American explorer Charles Hall tried to reach the North Pole in 1871. But he died on the way there. From hypothermia? No – it was from arsenic poisoning. Was it murder or an accident? No one knows.

OOPS!

BLOWING HOT AIR

At the beginning of the 1900s, the race was on to reach the poles. Smart explorers set out with ships, kayaks or dog sleighs. One not-so-smart group took a hot air balloon. Swedish explorer S. A. Andrée and two pals took to the sky in 1897. No one knew what happened until about 30 years later, when their diaries and photographs were found. The balloon had crash-landed just two days into the flight.

A member of Andrée's crew took this photo of the crash.

DOGS VERSUS PONIES

Norwegian explorer Roald Amundsen had wanted to get to the North Pole first. But Robert Peary from the United States beat him to it – or at least thought he did. Luckily for Amundsen, Earth has two poles, so he simply headed for the South Pole in 1910 instead. There, he faced off against yet another Robert, the British explorer Robert Scott.

If only Robert Scott had been a skier or a dog lover. Amundsen travelled on skis while sled dogs pulled his supplies. Scott took a few dogs, but he also brought ponies and large motorized sledges. Heavy machinery wasn't the best match for ice, though. One of the heavy sledges fell through the ice and sank before the expedition had even begun. The others broke down. The ponies all died as well.

Scott and his men ended up trudging along. They dragged most of their supplies behind them on ordinary sledges, pulling them along themselves instead of using dogs. They arrived at the South Pole only to see the Norwegian flag already there. They were about a month too late. Amundsen's dogs were the winners!

The ponies Robert Scott brought along were supposed to pull most of the supplies. Instead, none of them survived.

DID YOU KNOW?

Englishman Ernest Shackleton's ship got stuck in the Antarctic ice in 1915. Miraculously, all the men escaped alive. But when they all were finally rescued two years later, they learned just how out of touch they were. They had no idea that World War I was still raging in Europe.

Shackleton left most of his crew on Elephant Island while he set out in a lifeboat.

FAST FACT

Apsley Cherry-Garrard, a British zoologist, tagged along with Robert Scott's expedition to gather penguin eggs. The Antarctic proved to be so cold that Cherry-Garrard couldn't stop his teeth from chattering. By the time he returned home, many of them were shattered!

MADDENING MOUNTAINS

ELUSIVE EVEREST

New Zealander Edmund Hillary and Tenzing Norgay from Nepal reached the top of Mount Everest in 1953. Decades before this success, British climber George Mallory tried and failed three times. Climbers had discovered that they needed bottled oxygen to survive at such great heights. But Mallory thought that was cheating. He disappeared on the mountain in 1924. Who said cheats never win?

In 1933 Frank Smythe missed the top of Mount Everest by just 300 metres (1,000 feet). During the climb he took photos of tracks that supposedly belonged to the mythical yeti. But the Museum of Natural History in London concluded the footprints didn't belong to a large supernatural apelike creature that walks on two legs – it was just a bear.

The remains of George Mallory (left) were finally found on Mount Everest 75 years after he vanished.

The New Zealand Northern Survey Party meant to climb Shapeless Mountain in Antarctica in 1957. But they climbed the wrong peak! Having a sense of humour about their error, they decided to call the new mountain they discovered Mistake.

OOPS!

A MOUNTAIN MYSTERY

Some blame yetis for the demise of a group of climbers in Dyatlov Pass in the Ural Mountains of Russia in 1959. The hikers seem to have fled their tent in a panic before dying. Other conspiracy theorists think aliens in UFOs killed them!

Another name for the mythical yeti is "The Abominable Snowman".

DID YOU KNOW?

Achoo! Whilst having a snack during an expedition up Nanga Parbat in Pakistan, British climber Alan Hinkes got flour up his nose. He sneezed so violently that he injured his back. He had to quit the climb.

DARK DEPTHS

EYE SPY

The world's oceans remain almost entirely unmapped and unex
The effort to examine the oceans pits explorers against darkness an
extreme pressures. Americans William Beebe and Otis Barton trave
more than 0.8 kilometres (0.5 miles) down into the sea off the coas
Bermuda in 1934. Their vessel, called a bathysphere, looked like a la
metal eyeball. They had no camera. The glowing creatures they des
were so bizarre that people thought they'd made them up!

In 1960 American Don Walsh and Swiss engineer Jacques Picca
became the first to reach Mariana Trench. It is the world's deepest p
located in the Pacific Ocean. On the way down, the two men heard
giant bang! A window had cracked. But the expedition continued.

The detailed illustrations created from
Beebe (right) and Otis Barton's (left) des
were published in *National Geograp*

Sometimes even robots can't handle the pressure. The deep-sea robot Nereus imploded while exploring a trench near New Zealand in 2014.

OOPS!

SUNKEN TREASURE

Some ocean explorers dream of treasure. On Oak Island in Canada, a strange shaft in the ground has attracted attention. Did pirates bury gold there? Treasure seekers have spent millions of pounds trying to find out but haven't unearthed anything interesting.

Shipwrecks, however, have turned up amazing artifacts. In 1988 American Tommy Thompson found the legendary Ship of Gold, which sank off the southeast coast of the United States in 1857. He was supposed to split the prize with his crew and backers, but instead he grabbed the treasure and ran! Police spent years trying to track him down.

Thompson was eventually caught in 2015.

DID YOU KNOW?

American explorer John Cleves Symmes Jr. thought people could enter the inside of Earth through holes at the North Pole and South Pole. The United States Congress actually voted to fund an expedition to look for the holes in 1822. But the trip never happened.

INTO THE SKY

OFF THE GRID

Explorers have taken to the skies in planes, balloons, gliders and even garden chairs. Not all of these adventures were roaring successes. Perhaps the most famous bad day in airborne exploration is when American Amelia Earhart vanished in 1937. She was attempting to fly around the world. Some people claim her disappearance was faked, and she took on a new life and new name. More likely, her plane ran out of fuel and she either crashed into the sea or was left stranded on a deserted island in the Pacific.

Neither Amelia Earhart nor her Lockheed Electra plane have been found, and her disappearance fascinates people today.

Larry Walters always wanted to be a US Air Force pilot. So in 1982 he tied 42 weather balloons to his garden chair. Instead of floating up slowly, he shot 4,900 metres (16,000 feet) into the air! On the way back down, he got caught in some power lines, knocking out an entire neighbourhood's electricity.

OOPS!

Square windows work fine on a house but not in an aeroplane. Sharp corners break easily under stress. The engineers who built the de Havilland Comet jet apparently forgot this important fact. In 1954 two of the brand new aeroplanes burst apart in mid air.

SUPERNATURAL SEA?

The Bermuda Triangle, an area of the Atlantic Ocean just off the coast of Florida, supposedly swallows up travellers. A squadron of military planes from the United States that disappeared in 1945 helped to popularize the myth. Several other disappearances kept the legend alive. Some have even claimed the lost city of Atlantis lies beneath the Triangle. Apparently the city's "special energy crystals" are to blame for the area's weirdness. But ships and planes regularly pass through the area without incident.

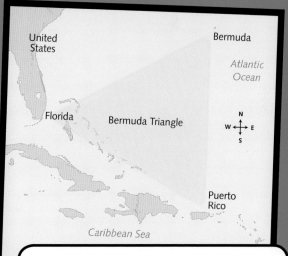

Most disappearances and sunken ships attributed to the Bermuda Triangle actually happened somewhere else in the Atlantic Ocean.

DID YOU KNOW?

The world's first aeroplane lasted only one day. After the Wright brothers made their historic flight in America in 1903, a strong gust of wind knocked over their plane and wrecked it.

ROCKET SCIENCE

SUPERSTITIOUS TOILET BREAKS

Space was the final frontier for human exploration. Yuri Gagarin of the Soviet Union became the first person in space in 1961. On the way to the launch pad, he asked the bus to stop so he could get out and go to the toilet. To this day Russian cosmonauts bound for space always stop to pee before blasting off.

BEAVERS ON THE MOON

Long before Gagarin's historic flight, people wondered what might be out in space. In 1835 a newspaper in New York reported that a famous astronomer had observed life on the moon. His discoveries included intelligent beavers, people with wings and blue goats. The story was a ridiculous hoax, but many believed it.

After his trip to space, Yuri Gagarin became a national hero in the Soviet Union.

THE REAL MOON LANDING

The moon landing, on the other hand, was no hoax. Americans Neil Armstrong and Buzz Aldrin really walked on the moon in 1969. But some people think this never happened. They say the US government filmed the whole thing in a movie studio. If they did, perhaps they should have included some beavers?

OOPS!

As Neil Armstrong climbed out of the Lunar Module, he accidentally broke off a very important switch. Whoops – they needed to flip that switch to take off and return home! No big deal. Armstrong used a ballpoint pen to flip the broken stub.

Luckily, Armstrong was able to repair the switch he broke when descending from the Lunar Module. Good thing, otherwise he may have been stuck on the moon!

DID YOU KNOW

When Neil Armstrong stepped onto the moon, he was supposed to say, "One small step for a man, one giant leap for mankind." But many think it sounded as though he said, "One small step for man, one giant leap for mankind" instead. Was the word *a* left out? Armstrong insists he said it – it's just his accent that's to blame.

Don't drop that! In 2003 factory workers in the United States had to move NOAA-19, a weather satellite, to put on the finishing touches. But they forgot to bolt it down to its cart. The satellite crashed to the floor, breaking many important components.

OOPS!

NO CALLER ID?

Space blunders and mistakes continue to this day. British astronaut Tim Peake accidentally dialled a wrong number from the International Space Station in 2015. He said, "Hello, is this planet Earth?" The woman on the other end must have thought she'd received a prank call!

The International Space Station has been home to various crew members since 2000.

FAST FACT

Mars was the Bermuda Triangle of space during the 1990s. NASA lost three spacecraft. The Mars Observer, the Mars Polar Lander and the Mars Climate Orbiter were all destroyed before making it to the surface of Mars.

Exercise in space is also a challenge. Astronauts have to strap themselves in when aboard the International Space Station, just like Sunita Williams did in 2012.

WAFTING WASABI

Getting used to daily life without gravity can be challenging. Food and drinks don't stay put. Early astronauts sucked both food and drinks out of pouches with straws. Now freeze-dried food comes in packages Velcroed to a tray that is strapped to the wall or a person's lap.

In 2007 US astronaut Sunita Williams was preparing a space version of sushi when the wasabi escaped. The spicy sauce floated around in little blobs and stuck to the walls. The crew managed to clean it up. But they didn't use wasabi again.

SPACE TOILETS

Going to the toilet in space is an adventure too. Today's International Space Station astronauts use a special toilet that costs as much as £14 million. Early astronauts just had to hold it. In 1961 launch preparations turned a 15-minute space trip into an hours-long wait for US astronaut Alan Shepherd. He eventually had to pee inside his space suit! Thankfully, the oxygen flowing through the suit dried up the puddle within minutes.

FUN FACTS

For an explorer, Christopher Columbus from Italy wasn't all that observant. While sailing near the Dominican Republic in 1493, Columbus caught sight of three mermaids. Except they were really manatees. Columbus noted in his journal that the so-called mermaids were "not so beautiful as they are said to be."

After noticing some streams in Australia that flowed inland, Frank Hann went looking for a lake. He found one. Unfortunately, the lake had no water in it! It was a dry salt flat. Hann named his 1897 discovery Lake Disappointment.

American Truman Everts was exploring Yellowstone National Park in 1870 when he became separated from his group. He made a knife from a buckle and a fishhook from a pin. He ate mostly thistles. After surviving for more than a month in the wild, he was eventually rescued. His two rescuers first thought he was a wounded bear!

Norwegian Roald Amundsen made it to the North Pole in 1926 in an airship called a dirigible. It was much hardier than a hot air balloon. Some historians believe that he was first to reach both poles.

Most astronauts love to put hot sauce on their food. Why? It can be difficult to taste food in space. Scientists aren't sure why. One theory is that smells don't travel to the nose easily in near-zero gravity.

Do polar bears hunt penguins? No! The two animals live at opposite ends of Earth. Polar bears call the North Pole home, and penguins live near the South Pole. Explorers trying to reach the poles hunted and ate whatever they could catch.

Members of the exclusive Explorer's Club attended a dinner party in New York City, USA, in 1951. What was on the menu? Woolly mammoth! The extinct beast had supposedly been defrosted from glacial ice. However, recent research has shown that the meat was actually sea turtle.

Women weren't welcome on long sea voyages during the Age of Exploration (late 1400s to late 1700s). But that didn't stop Frenchwoman Jeanne Baret. She posed as a man named Jean and worked as a botanist on a 1766 expedition with French explorer Louis-Antoine de Bougainville. In Tahiti, though, her secret came out. She was the first woman to circle the globe.

GLOSSARY

arsenic poisonous chemical

avalanche large mass of ice, snow or earth that suddenly moves down the side of a mountain

cannibal person who eats the flesh of other human beings

dirigible aircraft inflated with a gas that is lighter than air and can be steered

expedition journey with a goal, such as exploring or searching for something

extinction complete disappearance of a species

gravity force that pulls objects with mass together; gravity pulls objects down toward the centre of Earth

hoax trick to make people believe something that is not true

lichen flat, mosslike plant that grows on trees and rocks

malaria serious disease that people get from mosquito bites; malaria causes high fever, chills and sometimes death

mutiny revolt against the captain of a ship

navigation using instruments and charts to find your way in a ship or other vehicle

parasite animal or plant that lives on or inside another animal or plant and causes harm

piranha flesh-eating fish with very sharp teeth

ransom money or objects that are demanded before someone who is being held captive can be set free

satellite spacecraft that circles Earth; satellites gather and send information

scurvy deadly disease caused by lack of vitamin C; scurvy produces swollen limbs, bleeding gums and weakness

voyage long journey

FIND OUT MORE

BOOKS

Explorer (DK Eyewitness Books), Rupert Matthews (Dorling Kindersley, 2012).

New Worlds (Explorer Tales), Nick Hunter (Raintree, 2013).

The Story of Space: Space Stations, Steve Parker (Franklin Watts, 2015).

WEBSITES

BBC: Exploration
http://www.bbc.co.uk/science/space/universe/exploration/
Discover the exploration of the universe in both history and today.

Royal Museums Geeenwich: Exploration & Endeavour
http://www.rmg.co.uk/discover/explore/exploration-endeavour
Travel the globe with famous expolorers.

FURTHER RESEARCH

Explorers come from many different nations and backgrounds. What can you learn about women and non-Europeans who contributed to world exploration? Try searching online or asking a librarian for help.

Who really discovered America? Some historians disagree on who deserves credit for bringing knowledge of the new continent to the rest of the world. Look up Christopher Columbus, Leif Eriksson and Zheng He online. Then decide for yourself.

PLACES TO VISIT

National Maritime Museum
Greenwich
London
SE10 9NF
+44 (0)208 312 6608
Email: bookings@rmg.co.uk
Visit this fascinating museum to find out more about some of history's most famous and intrepid explorers and the ships they sailed in. There are lots of interesting activities for kids – and you may even be asked to Walk The Plank!

The National Space Centre
Exploration Drive
Leicester
LE4 5NS
+44 (0)116 261 0261
info@spacecentre.co.uk
The Space Centre gives you the chance to discover how it feels to be an astronaut on a space mission, with a unique 3D simulator experience, a 42-metre high Rocket Tower and six interactive galleries.

INDEX